T5-AAP-457

WELCOME TO BIG BAAN!

THERE ARE BIRDS APLENTY IN THE GREAT FOREST OF **BIG BAAN** BUT NONE AS POPULAR AS...

Ma, it's Kalia!

YES, KALIA...THE WISE AND FRIENDLY CROW!

HIS BEST FRIENDS ARE KEECHU AND MEECHU FROM THE LOST COLONY OF RABBITS....

.... AND SHONAR, THE DEER.

HE SOMETIMES ENCOUNTERS *BIG BAAN'S* GROUCHIEST RESIDENT, BABLOO, THE BEAR WHOSE SOLE PASSION IN LIFE IS TO GATHER HONEY.

AND HE FREQUENTLY CLASHES WITH THE WILY JACKAL, CHAMATAKA AND HIS BUMBLING SIDEKICK, DOOB DOOB, THE CROCODILE.

YES, THERE ARE WILD AND WHACKY THINGS HAPPENING IN **BIG BAAN** !

HONEY IN THE LOG

AND INDEED, KALIA WAS DOING HIS BEST.

I WON'T LET YOU GO IN.

PECK ME AS MUCH AS YOU WANT. BUT YOU CANNOT STOP ME.

I'LL HAVE A GOOD LUNCH TODAY. HEE! HEE! HEE!

WHAT SHOULD I DO?

HERE COMES BABLOO. BUT THAT NASTY FELLOW WILL NEVER STOP TO HELP ME OR THE RABBITS, UNLESS...UNLESS...

CHAMATAKA, PLEASE BRING SOME HONEY FOR ME TOO, WILL YOU?

HONEY DID YOU SAY? WHERE'S THE HONEY?

IN THIS HOLLOW LOG. THERE'S PLENTY OF IT. BUT YOU'LL HAVE TO PUSH THAT STONE ASIDE.

8

FUN WITH SHADOWS

You will need: A table-lamp; a bare wall for a screen and your hands, of course!

You can have a poultry show in your house!

Stand a few feet away from a wall and arrange your hands and fingers in front of a lamp as shown, to make the shadow of a hen.

A rooster needs a comb. You'll have to cut it out from a piece of stiff paper and hold it up as shown.

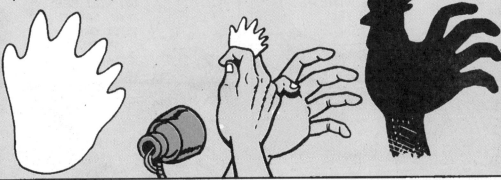

You need a cut-out for he chicken too. Make sure you cut out a hole where its eye should be.

THE AMBUSH!

HEY, DOOB-DOOB!

HELLO!

I KNOW HOW WE CAN CATCH A NICE FAT DEER.

YOU DO?

I LOVE DEER!

SO DO I.

WHAT'S YOUR PLAN?

COME WITH ME. I'LL TELL YOU.

DO YOU SEE THAT LARGE ROCK OVER THERE?

YES.

I'VE NOTICED SEVERAL DEER GOING PAST IT.

I'M NO GOOD AT CATCHING DEER ON SHORE, CHAMATAKA.

THEY RUN AWAY BEFORE I CAN OPEN MY MOUTH.

YOU DON'T HAVE TO OPEN YOUR MOUTH.

12

THE JUNGLE SCHOOL

BY
LUIS M. FERNANDES
AND
PRADEEP SATHE

TREES ARE SO USEFUL. THEY PROVIDE FOOD AND SHADE AND SHELTER.

AND THEY PREVENT FLOODS.

PREVENT FLOODS?

HOW CAN TREES PREVENT FLOODS?

WHEN RAIN STRIKES THE GROUND FORCEFULLY, IT LOOSENS THE SOIL. THE WATER CARRIES THE SOIL AWAY...

...AND DUMPS IT INTO A RIVER.

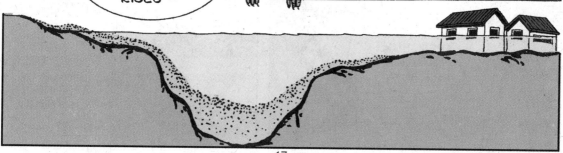

AS MORE AND MORE MUD IS DUMPED INTO THE RIVER, THE BED OF THE RIVER RISES...

AND THE WATER OVERFLOWS THE BANKS AND FLOODS THE COUNTRYSIDE.

18

HOW SOIL IS FORMED

IN THE BEGINNING, THERE WAS NO MUD OR SOIL AS WE SHOULD CALL IT, ON EARTH. THE LAND WAS NOTHING BUT HARD ROCK AND NOTHING COULD GROW. THEN SLOWLY OVER THE AGES, THE ACTION OF SUN, WIND AND RAIN CAUSED THE ROCKS ON THE SURFACE TO CRUMBLE INTO SAND, GRAVEL AND DUST.

OUR SOIL TODAY IS MADE UP OF SAND, GRAVEL AND DUST AND. THE REMAINS OF DEAD PLANTS AND ANIMALS.

IF SOIL IS ALLOWED TO BE WASHED AWAY BY THE RAIN, OR BLOWN AWAY BY THE WIND, FARMERS WILL NOT BE ABLE TO RAISE CROPS AND TREES WON'T GROW.

BESIDES, THE SOIL WHICH IS WASHED AWAY FINALLY ENDS UP IN RIVERS AND MAY CAUSE FLOODS.

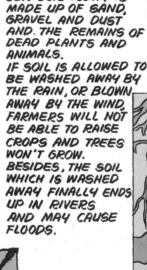

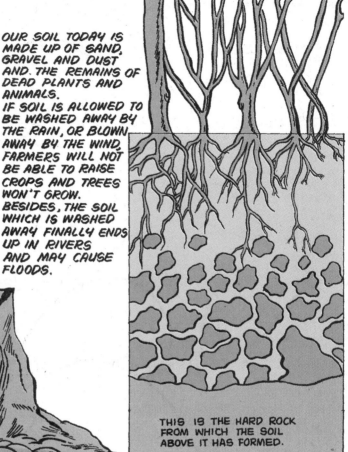

THIS IS THE HARD ROCK FROM WHICH THE SOIL ABOVE IT HAS FORMED.

RAIN HAS WASHED AWAY ALL THE SOIL FROM THIS HILLSIDE. NOTHING CAN GROW HERE NOW. GRADUALLY THE ROCKS WILL START BREAKING UP TO FORM NEW SOIL. BUT THE PROCESS IS VERY, VERY SLOW. EVEN AFTER 600 YEARS ONLY ABOUT AN INCH OF SOIL MAY BE FORMED.

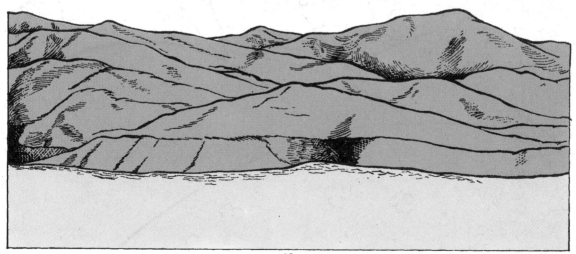

COLOUR THE PICTURE

MEET THE SLOTH BEAR

Based on
material
provided by
Nandini Deshmukh

Script: Ashvin

Illustrations:
Pradeep Sathe

BHALU PEERS LAZILY OUT OF HER CAVE. AS USUAL, SHE'S BEEN SLEEPING ALL THROUGH THE HOT SUMMER'S DAY.

SHE'S READY TO GO OUT IN SEARCH OF FOOD.

BUT NOW, THE SUN IS ABOUT TO SET, AND IT'S MUCH COOLER.

BHALU LOOKS LAZY AND CLUMSY AND CANNOT SEE OR HEAR VERY WELL; BUT SHE IS VERY STRONG. SHE CAN WALK MILES TO FIND THE FOOD SHE LIKES.

WHAT'S THE MATTER? SHE HAS STOPPED AND SHE'S SNIFFING HARD! M-M-M-M!

IT'S A BEE-HIVE! SHE HAS FOUND HONEY! UP THE TREE SHE SWIFTLY CLAMBERS, GRIPPING ITS TRUNK...

...WITH HER SHARP CURVED CLAWS AND THE ROUGH SOLES OF HER PAWS.

THWACK

WHAT A POWERFUL BLOW!

M-M-M-M! IT'S DELICIOUS! BHALU LOVES HONEY.

SHE'S EATEN EVERY DROP OF THE HONEY BUT SHE'S STILL HUNGRY! SO SHE SHUFFLES UP TO ANOTHER TREE...

...AND SHAKES IT WITH ALL HER MIGHT.

NOW WHO IS THIS STRANGER? WILL BHALU DRIVE HIM AWAY?

NOT AT ALL. HE'S COME TO LIVE WITH HER AND BHALU GIVES HIM A WARM WELCOME.

BHALU AND HER MATE FIND THE SUMMER HEAT QUITE UNBEARABLE. WHAT'S WORSE, THEY ARE THIRSTY AND THERE IS NO WATER IN THE RIVER. BUT THEY DON'T GIVE UP. THEY WILL DIG UP THE RIVER-BED...

...TILL THEY FIND WATER.

SOME TIME LATER HER MATE GOES AWAY. BHALU DOES NOT STOP HIM. LIVING ALONE DOES NOT BOTHER HER. SHE LIKES IT.

SHE DIGS UP THE TERMITE MOUNDS WITH HER LONG CLAWS.

SOON THE RAINS COME. AND RAINS FOR BHALU MEAN PLENTY OF TERMITES — HER FAVOURITE INSECT FOOD.

22

SHE HUFFS AND PUFFS AND BLOWS AWAY ALL THE DUST AND EARTH TILL SHE CAN SEE THE INSECTS IN THEIR GALLERIES.

SU-R-R-R! WHAT'S THAT SOUND? IT CAN BE HEARD 4ARDS AWAY! SHE'S SUCKING THE TERMITES INTO HER MOUTH!

SEE HOW CLEVERLY SHE HAS ROLLED UP HER UPPER LIP TO COVER HER NOSTRILS SO THAT THE DUST CAN'T ENTER THEM!

OF COURSE, SHE'S LUCKY THAT SHE HAS A TOOTHLESS GAP IN HER UPPER JAW OR SHE COULDN'T HAVE SUCKED IN THOSE TERMITES!

WHEN THE RAINY SEASON IS OVER, BHALU SWIMS ACROSS THE RIVER TO RAID THE SUGAR-CANE FIELDS ON THE OPPOSITE BANK.

AT LAST WINTER SETS IN. BHALU IS NOW A PROUD MOTHER.

SHE LOVINGLY CARES FOR HER HELPLESS CUBS TILL...

...THEIR EYES OPEN AND THEY ARE ABLE TO ROMP AND PLAY...

... AND JOIN HER IN HER WANDERINGS.

IT'S A TIGER! HOW DARE HE COME ANYWHERE NEAR HER CUBS!

WHAT IS THAT STRANGE SCENT?

BHALU BRISTLES WITH RAGE. SHE SNARLS AND GROWLS.

SILENTLY THE TIGER SLINKS AWAY.

BUT BHALU DOES NOT TRUST HIM. SHE SHARPENS HER CLAWS JUST IN CASE HE DECIDES TO RETURN.

WHEN THEY ARE ABOUT THREE YEARS OLD, THE CUBS WANDER AWAY LIKE THEIR FATHER.

BUT THEY MUST BE WARY OR THEY MIGHT GET CAUGHT AND END UP PERFORMING TRICKS ON THE ROAD OR IN A CIRCUS.

YOU HAVE MET THE SLOTH BEAR. HERE ARE SOME OF ITS COUSINS FOUND IN OTHER PARTS OF THE WORLD.

THE WHITE POLAR BEAR

THE GIGANTIC KODIAK BEAR

THE SPECTACLED BEAR

THE SLEEK SUN BEAR

CHAMATAKA IN TROUBLE!

DOOB-DOOB, YOU AND I COULD MAKE A WONDERFUL TEAM. BUT YOU MUST LEARN TO HUNT.

I CAN HUNT VERY WELL, THANK YOU.

ONLY IN THE RIVER. YOU COULDN'T CATCH A FLY ON LAND. WHAT IF THE RIVER WERE TO DRY UP ONE DAY? YOU'D STARVE TO DEATH.

!!

IS IT...ER... DIFFICULT TO HUNT ON LAND?

IT'S NOT EASY. BUT I'LL TEACH YOU THE SECRETS.

WE JACKALS ARE BORN HUNTERS. I CAN SPOT MY PREY A MILE AWAY.

THEN HOW'S THAT I'VE NEVER SEEN YOU CATCH ANYTHING?

SSSSSH! A FROG!

WATCH HOW I CATCH IT.

GOT YOU!

SEE HOW EASY IT WAS! YOU COULD CATCH BIGGER ANIMALS IN THE SAME WAY.

COME OUT, YOU!

???

ER...CHAMATAKA...I...DON'T THINK...THAT'S A FROG.

Y-YOU'RE RIGHT!

S-SO SORRY, FRIEND. I THOUGHT YOU WERE SOME-ONE ELSE...HEH-HEH!

ER...CHAMATAKA, I THINK I'VE LEARNT ENOUGH TODAY.

G-GOODBYE.

HELP!

26

it's easy to make!

A MAGNETIC LADY BUG FOR YOUR FRIDGE

YOU WILL NEED

A BOTTLE CAP, PUPPET EYES(YOU GET THES[E]
AT ANY STATIONERY STORE), A PENCIL, GLU[E]
A PAINTBRUSH, SMALL MAGNET, FABRIC
COLOURS.

CLEAN THE BOTTLE CAP.

DIVIDE IT INTO THREE PARTS WITH BLACK PENCIL,
AND COLOUR IT AS SHOWN IN THE PICTURE.

NOW COLOUR THE REMAINING PART RED AND
LET IT DRY.

STICK ON THE EYES AND PAINT THE BLACK
SPOTS IN AREAS SHOWN.

STICK THE MAGNET ON THE BACK OF
THE BOTTLE CAP. YOUR LADY BUG IS
READY TO CRAWL UP YOUR FRIDGE!

MAKE YOUR OWN JAPANESE GARDEN

You will need:

1. A wide bowl
2. A piece of glass
3. Light blue paper
4. Mud
5. Tiny plants – like ferns and those that look like mini-trees.
6. Some pebbles and stones.
7. Some tiny plastic figures and animals and birds. Also a small toy bridge or house if you have them.

All you have to do is:

Keep the piece of glass in the bowl with the sheet of light blue paper under it. Spread mud all over the glass except in the centre where you want to show the pond. Plant the ferns and mini-trees in the mud. Place the pebbles and stones at various places.

Arrange the people, birds, animals and the house and the boat in the garden. You could also make a small bridge and place it across the pond.

Now your Japanese Garden is ready. Show it to your friends and they will all want to make one as well!

CATCH ME IF YOU CAN!

THERE'S KALIA! I WONDER WHOM HE IS LOOKING AT.

HE IS LOOKING AT BABLOO...

...WHO'S UP IN THE TREE GATHERING HONEY!

THROW DOWN SOME HONEY FOR US, BABLOO, OLD FRIEND!

ZOOM

THUD

AS I WAS SAYING, KALIA AND BABLOO ARE OUR GREATEST ENEMIES.

I BELIEVE YOU NOW.

COTTON BOLLS, ANYONE?

THESE COTTON BOLLS, MY UNCLE GAVE ME ARE SO SOFT AND FLUFFY.

THEY'LL MAKE MY NEST VERY COMFORTABLE.

HELP! HELP!

OH, OH, MY FRIENDS ARE IN TROUBLE.

BLOCK THE OTHER END DOOB-DOOB.

THEY'RE TRAPPED!

YES, I'LL GO IN AND BRING THEM OUT... HEH-HEH.

I'VE GOT TO SAVE THEM... BUT HOW?

35

Tinkle Tinkle little book
The only one through which I look
Clever Kalia is the best
Dull Doob Doob is a pest.
Rakesh Handa
Bombay 400 061
Tinkle 18 published in May 1982

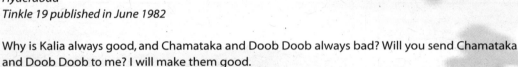

I went to a painting competition conducted by the
Forest Department and in that I drew wildlife from
Tinkle (Kalia), and I got the second prize for it.
N. Vijay Varma
Hyderabad
Tinkle 19 published in June 1982

Why is Kalia always good, and Chamataka and Doob Doob always bad? Will you send Chamataka
and Doob Doob to me? I will make them good.
Shardul P. Ramaiya
Bombay
Tinkle 20 published in August 1982

I am a regular reader of TINKLE. I like Kalia, the Crow very much. I think it is a very interesting
magazine. I read the stories from TINKLE and narrate them to my younger sister.
Mustaq Raza
Guntakal
Tinkle 24 published in November 1982

I think that Chamataka does not get any of the animals to eat because Kalia, the Crow spoils all
plans of Chamataka. So I think that Chamataka will die of hunger and you will not get any more
stories of Kalia.
K. Shailu
Orissa
Tinkle 26 published in January 1983

In several Tinkle issues I have seen Chamataka being
thrown by Babloo. If things continue this way, Chamataka
will die pretty soon. Remember to call me to his funeral!
Rita Sharma
Gangtok
Tinkle 75 published in January 1985

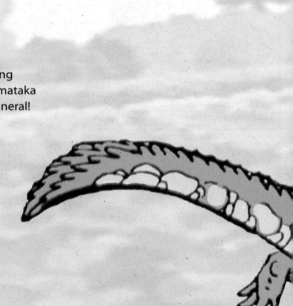

Every night I dream that I'm in TINKLE WORLD
And talking with Kalia
And Chamataka, Doob Doob and Babloo.
Vikas B. Naik
Bombay
Tinkle 35 published in May 1983

Will Kalia ever have a wife?
Or will he remain a bachelor all his life?
Harish Dantale
56 A.P.O
Tinkle 35 published in May 1983

We were to have a debate in class and the topic was: " Forest Trees Should Be Cut Down". I was elected captain of the opposition. So I visited several bookstalls to get a book covering this topic, but I had no luck. I bought TINKLE NO 31 however, and took it home. When I came to JUNGLE SCHOOL featuring Kalia and his friends, there was my topic! Here I was prepared to spend Rs 20 on a book and Kalia told me all I wanted to know for just Rs 3. We won the debate!
Rohit Jinandaney
Bombay
Tinkle 39 published in July 1983

Why don't you publish a super poster of Kalia, Doob Doob, Chamataka and Babloo?
Saponti Baroowa
Golaghat
Tinkle 46 published in November 1982

Why does Chamataka always catch Keechu and Meechu? Aren't there any other rabbits in the forest?
Sunita Varrier
Bombay
Tinkle 56 published in April 1984

If you ask my opinion about TINKLE I will say that it is the most knowledgeable, interesting and funny book in the whole world. Doob Doob is very funny though I feel sorry for him sometimes when Kalia outwits him.
'Meet the Animal' is also very interesting.
K. Madhuri Pai
New Delhi
Tinkle 31 published in March 20, 1983

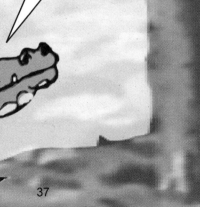

WHAT DOES SHE MEAN KALIA OUTWITS ME! HOW CAN A BIRDBRAIN OUTSMART A CROC!

THE GOLDEN EAGLE IS FOUND IN SEVERAL PLACES NORTH OF THE EQUATOR WHERE THERE ARE MOUNTAINS.

MEET THE

GOLDEN EAGLE

Script : Ashvin

Illustrations : Pradeep Sathe

IN INDIA THEY ARE FOUND IN THE HIMALAYAS AT A HEIGHT OF 1220 METRES.

THEY LIVE IN PAIRS. HERE IS A PAIR SOARING MAJESTICALLY IN THE AIR. THEY DON'T FLAP THEIR WINGS TOO MUCH, BUT JUST GLIDE IN THE AIR. IN THIS WAY THEY AVOID TIRING THEMSELVES AND THEY CAN STAY UP FOR HOURS TOGETHER.

EACH PAIR LIVES AND HUNTS IN A TERRITORY OF ABOUT 32 SQ. Km.

THIS MAGPIE HAS WANDERED INTO THEIR TERRITORY.

ONE OF THE EAGLES DIVES AT TERRIFIC SPEED WITH HALF-FOLDED WINGS...

...REACHES OUT WITH ITS TALONS...

...AND GRABS THE BIRD.

THE DEAD BIRD IS TAKEN TO A FAVOURITE EATING PLACE.

WELL DONE, HIS MATE SEEMS TO SAY.

SHE IS LARGER AND HEAVIER THAN HIM.

THEY PLUCK THEIR PREY WITH THEIR HOOKED BEAKS, RIP THE FLESH INTO PIECES AND SWALLOW THEM WHOLE.

BUT THE MAGPIE WAS TOO SMALL. HERE THEY GO AGAIN LOOKING FOR MORE FOOD.

A MAN LOOKING DOWN FROM A HELICOPTER WOULD NOT SEE ANYTHING ON THE GROUND HERE. BUT THE EAGLES HAVE SEEN A RABBIT. THEY CAN SEE WELL EVEN FROM A DISTANCE OF 250 METRES.

AS THE PREY IS BIG AND HEAVY, IT IS THE LARGER BIRD, THE FEMALE, WHO DIVES THIS TIME.

SHE DESCENDS RAPIDLY, AND USING A COVERED APPROACH...

...TAKES HER PREY BY SURPRISE. THE GRIP OF HER DEADLY TALONS, KILLS THE RABBIT AT ONCE.

SHE COVERS THE PREY WITH HER WINGS. SHE IS NOT TRYING TO HIDE IT FROM ANYONE. IT'S A COMMON PRACTICE AMONG EAGLES TO COVER THE PREY WITH THEIR WINGS. LATER SHE CARRIES THE RABBIT TO THEIR EATING PLACE AND BOTH SHE AND HER MATE HAVE A GOOD FEED.

AFTER EATING THEY SCRATCH THEIR BEAKS CLEAN ON THE BARK OF A TREE. THIS SCRATCHING KEEPS THEIR BEAKS SHARP TOO.

ABOUT 6 TO 8 HOURS AFTER THE MEAL, THEY THROW THE BONES AND FUR OR FEATHERS OF THEIR PREY OUT THROUGH THE MOUTH, IN THE FORM OF A PELLET.

AS WE SAW, GOLDEN EAGLES ARE GREAT HUNTERS. BUT WHEN FOOD IS SCARCE, THEY DON'T HESITATE TO FEED ON DEAD ANIMALS IN THE COMPANY OF VULTURES.

THESE PELLETS SHOULD NOT BE MISTAKEN FOR THEIR DROPPINGS.

IN LATE MARCH THEY MAY FLY IN A PECULIAR STYLE. IT'S THEIR BREEDING SEASON. BOTH OF THEM, BUT ESPECIALLY THE MALE, DO ACROBATICS IN THE AIR...

...SOMETIMES THE MALE MAY TOSS A BIRD HE HAS CAUGHT TO THE FEMALE...

...SOMETIMES THEY MAY INTERLOCK CLAWS AND SPIRAL DOWNWARDS.

THEY USE THE SAME EYRIE (NEST) FOR YEARS AND YEARS. BUT EVERY BREEDING SEASON THEY ADD A FEW MORE TWIGS TO IT.

THEY FINALLY MATE ON THE GROUND.

THE FEMALE LAYS TWO EGGS.

THEN SHE AND HER MATE PROCEED TO HATCH THEM. HOWEVER, IT IS THE FEMALE WHO SITS ON THE EGGS MOST OF THE TIME.

THE EGGS HATCH IN ABOUT 40 DAYS.

THE CHICKS ARE GLUTTONOUS. FOR THE FIRST FEW DAYS THEIR PARENTS PUT FOOD INTO THEIR MOUTHS...

BUT LATER THEY BRING HALF-DEAD PREY AND GIVE LESSONS TO THE YOUNG ONES ON HOW TO USE THEIR TALONS AND BEAKS.

THEN COME LESSONS IN FLYING AND HUNTING. THIS PERIOD (ABOUT A YEAR) IS A DIFFICULT ONE FOR YOUNG EAGLES.

ONCE THE TRAINING PERIOD IS OVER, THE YOUNG ONES LEAVE THEIR PARENTS AND THEIR TERRITORY. AND THE BOND BETWEEN THEM AND THEIR PARENTS IS BROKEN FOREVER.

IN OLDEN DAYS, SHEPHERDS OF CENTRAL ASIA USED TO KEEP TRAINED GOLDEN EAGLES.

THESE EAGLES WERE USED TO DRIVE AWAY WOLVES.

KITE FIGHT!

A KITE.

I'VE CAUGHT IT! IT'S MINE!

CHAMATAKA, I'VE CAUGHT A KITE.

LET'S FLY IT.

I HAVE BETTER THINGS TO DO THAN TO FLY KITES.

DON'T BOTHER ME.

THAT KITE COULD BE VERY USEFUL TO ME.

IN A STRONG BREEZE IT COULD TAKE ME UP INTO THE AIR IF I HUNG ON TO THE STRING.

I WON'T HAVE TO CLIMB TREES ANY MORE.

42

FIND THE ODD ONE OUT

ONE OF THE HOUSES IS DIFFERENT FROM THE OTHERS IN A VERY SMALL WAY. WHICH ONE?

A

B

C

D

E

F

Answer : House E has no bars across window.

45

PURR...RRR!

MEOWWW...

SOUNDS LIKE A KITTEN.

WHAT'S A KITTEN?

A KITTEN IS A YOUNG CAT.

OH!

BUT WHAT'S A CAT?

A CAT IS A BIG KITTEN.

YOU ARE SO CLEVER, CHAMATAKA. YOU KNOW EVERYTHING.

THERE IT IS!

LOOKS LIKE A BABY TIGER.

HELLO, ARE YOU LOST?

DON'T BE AFRAID. WE WON'T EAT YOU.

I'M GOING TO MY COUSIN'S HOUSE.

MEET THE CAT

Script : Ashvin
Illustrations : Pradeep Sathe

CATS ARE BEAUTIFUL AND GRACEFUL ANIMALS. KEEPING ONE AS A PET CAN BE A REWARDING EXPERIENCE.

THE KITTEN YOU BRING HOME SHOULD BE ABOUT 2 MONTHS OLD. IT'LL BE NERVOUS AND UNFRIENDLY FOR A FEW DAYS...

...BUT IF YOU TREAT IT WELL AND GIVE IT REAL AFFECTION, IT WILL SOON MAKE ITSELF COMFORTABLE.

AS EVERYONE KNOWS, CATS ARE VERY FOND OF MILK GIVE YOUR CAT A SAUCER OF MILK TWICE A DAY.

COLLARS AND LEASHES ARE JUST NOT FOR THE CAT.

THEY NEED MEAT TOO AND THEY LOVE FISH.
BUT IT IS ADVISABLE TO COOK THE FISH BEFORE YOU GIVE IT TO YOUR KITTEN.

IF YOU'RE A STRICT VEGETARIAN, DON'T WORRY. YOUR CAT WILL LEARN TO CATCH MICE.

YOU CAN GIVE YOUR CAT CHAPATIS, OR BREAD, BUT DON'T GIVE IT COOKED RICE. SOME CATS ARE FOND OF VEGETABLES, SOME ARE NOT. DON'T FORCE YOUR KITTEN TO EAT ANYTHING IT DOESN'T LIKE.

IF YOU LIVE IN A MULTI-STOREYED BUILDING AND YOUR CAT CAN'T GO OUT FOR ITS TOILET THEN ARRANGE A LITTER BOX FILLED WITH SAND OR CHAFF. AFTER EVERY MEAL PICK YOUR KITTEN UP AND SET IT IN THE BOX. IT WILL SOON BE TOILET-TRAINED.

BUT PROVIDE IT WITH A BOWL OF CLEAN DRINKING WATER AT ALL TIMES.

CATS DON'T HAVE TO BE BATHED. THEY LICK THEIR BODIES CLEAN WITH THEIR ROUGH TONGUES:

TO CLEAN THEIR EYES AND SNOUT THEY USE THEIR PAWS.

BUT THEY NEED HELP TO REMOVE PAINT OR GREASE FROM THEIR FUR.

COMB AND BRUSH YOUR CAT'S FUR EVERYDAY. YOUR CAT WILL LOVE IT. USE A WIDE-TOOTHED COMB FOR THE PURPOSE.

WHILE BRUSHING IF YOU FIND TICKS OR FLEAS IN ITS FUR, REMOVE THEM CAREFULLY WITH A TWEEZER.

IF YOUR CAT DOESN'T GO OUT, KEEP A CARPET-COVERED POST WHICH IT CAN CLAW.

CATS KEEP THEIR CLAWS SHARP BY SCRATCHING.

TAKE A BOX OR A BASKET, LINE IT WITH A PIECE OF BLANKET OR RUG AND KEEP IT IN A CORNER. IT'S YOUR CAT'S BED.

CATS SELECT VERY ODD AND FUNNY PLACES TO REST ON. IT CAN BE A WINDOW LEDGE, OR THE TOP OF A SHELF, SOME PARTICULAR CHAIR OR EVEN YOUR BED, IF YOU ALLOW IT.

TRY CHANGING THE POSITION OF THE BASKET IF YOUR CAT REFUSES TO SLEEP IN IT.

NEVER TEASE YOUR CAT BY PULLING AT ITS EARS OR TAIL OR WHISKERS

..: AND IT HAS 30 SHARP TEETH IN ITS MOUTH— 16 IN THE UPPER JAW AND 14 IN THE LOWER JAW.

DON'T FORGET THAT YOUR CAT'S CUTE-LOOKING PAWS ARE WELL-EQUIPPED WITH RAZOR-SHARP CLAWS...

THE CAT IS CAPABLE OF USING BOTH THESE WEAPONS VERY EFFECTIVELY. REMEMBER, A CAT IS NOT AS TOLERANT AS A DOG.

ANOTHER THING ABOUT CATS — HOWEVER WELL YOU MAY TREAT THEM, THEY'LL NEVER OBEY YOU OR TREAT YOU AS MASTER OR MISTRESS.

SOMEDAY, HOWEVER, YOUR CAT MAY BRING YOU A GIFT, A DEAD MOUSE OR SOMETHING OF THAT SORT. DON'T SCOLD IT. IT'S JUST TRYING TO THANK YOU FOR BEING SO GOOD TO IT.

IN COURSE OF TIME, YOU'LL BEGIN TO UNDERSTAND ALL THE VARIOUS MOODS OF YOUR CAT...

DEMANDING FOOD

CURIOSITY

ANGRY AND READY TO ATTACK

AND YOU'LL GROW TO LOVE IT DESPITE ITS LACK OF DEVOTION TO YOU.

AT NIGHT YOUR CAT WILL WANT TO GO OUT. JUST FOR A STROLL OR TO HUNT MICE. SO BETTER KEEP A WINDOW OPEN.

THE CAT CAN SEE EVEN IN VERY DIM LIGHT, BECAUSE IT CAN OPEN THE PUPILS OF ITS EYES VERY WIDE TO LET IN WHATEVER LIGHT IS AVAILABLE.

IT USES ITS WHISKERS TO FEEL ITS WAY AROUND.

WHEN YOUR CAT IS SIX MONTHS OLD, IT WILL GO OUT AT NIGHT TO LOOK FOR A MATE.

...AND TOMCATS IN THE AREA WILL RUSH TOWARDS HER.

IF IT'S A FEMALE, SHE'LL MAKE A PECULIAR SOUND (KNOWN AS "CALLING"). THIS SOUND CAN BE HEARD OVER A GREAT DISTANCE...

SOMETIMES TWO OR THREE TOMCATS GATHER TOGETHER AND FIGHT FEROCIOUSLY.

TINKLE

51

YOUR CAT WILL BE PREGNANT FOR ABOUT 60 DAYS. DURING THIS PERIOD YOU'LL HAVE TO GIVE HER MORE FOOD—ESPECIALLY MILK.

AT THE END OF THE SECOND MONTH, MAKE HER SLEEPING QUARTERS MORE COMFORTABLE. YOUR CAT OF COURSE, WILL RE-ARRANGE THE BED AS SHE WANTS.

AND ONE DAY SHE WILL BECOME VERY UNEASY. IT'S TIME TO DELIVER HER KITTENS. KEEP BOWLS OF MILK AND WATER READY FOR HER. IF SHE NEEDS YOUR HELP, SHE WILL ASK FOR IT. OTHERWISE, DON'T INTERFERE IN HER BUSINESS.

WITHIN TWO HOURS SHE'LL BE A MOTHER MANY PEOPLE THINK THAT THE MOTHER CAT EATS ONE OF HER KITTENS. IT'S NOT TRUE. SHE EATS THE SAC AND PLACENTA OF EACH KITTEN.

THE KITTENS' EYES ARE CLOSED FOR 3 WEEKS. THEIR MOTHER KEEPS THEM WELL FED AND CLEAN BY LICKING THEM.

IF SHE WANTS TO SHIFT, SHE CATCHES HER KITTENS BY A FLAP OF SKIN AT THE BACK OF THE NECK.

AFTER 3 WEEKS, THE KITTENS OPEN THEIR EYES AND BECOME VERY PLAYFUL AND MISCHIEVOUS.

HERE ARE SOME PEDIGREE BREEDS OF CATS:

Black Persian

Russian Blue

Chocolate Brown Siamese

White Persian

Tortoiseshell

Orange Siamese

EASY TO MAKE!

A CUP CAT

YOU WILL NEED

A PING PONG BALL, AN ICE CREAM CUP, A SATIN BOW, FABRIC PAINTS [BLACK AND YELLOW], A PAIR OF SCISSORS A PENCIL AND WHITE PAPER.

  CUT OUT TWO TRIANGULAR PIECES FROM THE WHITE PAPER, FOR THE EARS. USE BLACK FABRIC PAINT TO MAKE BLACK PATCHES ON BOTH EARS.

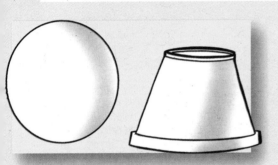

COLOUR THE BALL AND THE CUP WITH WHITE FABRIC PAINT.

PAINT EYES ON THE BALL AND MAKE BLACK SPLOTCHES ON THE CUP WITH BLACK FABRIC PAINT.

PAINT THE NOSE AND EYELASHES ON THE BALL.

PASTE THE BALL ON THE CUP, AND STICK ON THE EARS AND THE BOW. YOUR CUP CAT IS READY TO MEW!

THAT'S MY TREE!

GOOD NEWS, DOOB-DOOB!

HAVE YOU CAUGHT A DEER OR SOMETHING?

NO, NO! HOW CAN WE CATCH A DEER OR ANYTHING WHEN THAT PEST KALIA IS AROUND?

YOU'RE RIGHT.

I CAME TO TELL YOU THAT I KNOW WHERE HE LIVES.

WHERE?

ON THE TOP OF A TREE, NEAR BY.

OH, GOOD!

WE'LL HIDE IN HIS NEST AND WHEN HE COMES HOME... WHAM!

NEITHER OF US CAN CLIMB TREES, STUPID!

ER... THAT'S RIGHT.

SO HOW DO WE...

WE'LL BURN THE TREE DOWN!

WE'LL BE RID OF HIM FOREVER! HEEHEEHEE!

WHAT A GENIUS YOU ARE, CHAMATAKA! LET'S NOT WASTE ANY TIME!

WE'LL HAVE TO GET HOLD OF SOME FIRE FIRST.

SOMEBODY HAS LIT A FIRE OVER THERE! COME ON!

...THEN I CAUGHT THE TIGER BY THE THROAT AND SHOOK HIM AND SHOOK HIM TILL HE FAINTED.

ONCE I WRESTLED WITH AN ELEPHANT...

C-CROCODILE!

NOT CROCODILE, ELEPHANT!

T-THERE'S A C-CROCODILE, B-BEHIND YOU!

CROCODILE!

YIEEEIEEE!

THE JUNGLE SCHOOL

SCRIPT:
LUIS M. FERNANDES
ILLUSTRATIONS:
PRADEEP SATHE

CHAMATAKA, I'VE GOT A LETTER FROM ONE OF MY ADMIRERS.

YOUR ADMIRERS!

ARE YOU SURE IT'S FOR YOU AND NOT FOR ME?

I AM SURE! IT'S FROM A SWEET LITTLE GIRL.

SHE WRITES... YOU TOO, LISTEN, KALIA.

I'M LISTENING.

SHE WRITES: "MY DEAR DOOB-DOOB..."

DID YOU HEAR THAT?

YES, YES. GO ON!

"MY DEAR DOOB-DOOB, HOW DID YOU EVER GET SUCH STRONG BEAUTIFUL TEETH..."

STRONG, BEAUTIFUL TEETH? HEE HEE HEE!

HEE HEE HEE HOO HOO HOO!

HE'S JEALOUS!

WELL, AREN'T YOU GOING TO TELL OUR READERS HOW YOU CAME TO HAVE SUCH STRONG BEAUTIFUL TEETH...?

AH, YES!

MY TEETH ARE SO STRONG AND BEAUTIFUL BECAUSE I KEEP THEM CLEAN...

ALL YOU HAVE TO DO TO KEEP YOUR TEETH CLEAN IS TO KEEP YOUR MOUTH OPEN...

WHEN I DO THAT, TINY BIRDS HOP IN AND EAT THE BITS OF FOOD STUCK TO MY TEETH.

DO THEY CLEAN YOUR TEETH? I THOUGHT THEY CLEANED ONLY YOUR TONGUE.

ANYWAY, I DON'T THINK HUMAN BEINGS CAN CLEAN THEIR TEETH THAT WAY.

WHY NOT?

FOR ONE THING, THE BIRDS WOULD NEVER GO NEAR THEM. SECONDLY, THEIR MOUTHS ARE NOT AS LARGE AS YOURS.

HUMAN BEINGS KEEP THEIR TEETH CLEAN BY BRUSHING THEM WITH TOOTHPASTE OR TOOTH POWDER...

59

···TWICE A DAY.

TWICE? WHY SO MANY TIMES?

WELL, THEY EAT A LOT OF SWEETS AND STARCH.

THE SWEETS ESPECIALLY ARE VERY DANGEROUS. IF ALLOWED TO REMAIN IN THE MOUTH THEY PRODUCE ACIDS WHICH ROT THE TEETH.

SO MY ADMIRERS··· I MEAN OUR READERS, SHOULD NOT EAT SWEETS.

OH, THEY CAN EAT SWEETS.

BUT THEY SHOULD RINSE THEIR MOUTHS AFTER EATING THEM. AND BRUSH THEIR TEETH BEFORE GOING TO BED.

SO YOU SEE READERS, I HAVE SUCH STRONG BEAUTIFUL TEETH BECAUSE I KEEP THEM CLEAN.

···AND BECAUSE IF YOU LOSE A TOOTH, YOU GET ANOTHER ONE.

HUMAN BEINGS ARE NOT SO LUCKY. IF THEY LOSE A PERMANENT TOOTH THEY CAN'T GROW ANOTHER.

"MY DEAR DOOB DOOB, HOW DID YOU EVER GET SUCH STRONG BEAUTIFUL TEETH···"HEH-HEH.

ALL ABOUT TEETH

WHEN YOU SMILE, PEOPLE SEE THE CROWNS OF YOUR TEETH. NEITHER YOU NOR THEY CAN SEE THE ROOTS OF YOUR TEETH, AS THE ROOTS ARE HIDDEN BY THE GUMS

BUT EVERY TOOTH IS MADE UP OF A CROWN AND ROOT, OR ROOTS.

THE ROOTS HOLD THE TEETH IN PLACE IN THE JAW.

EVERY TOOTH HAS A SOFT CENTRE CALLED PULP.

THE PULP IS MADE OF NERVES AND BLOOD VESSELS.

THE PULP IS WELL PROTECTED BY A HARD SUBSTANCE CALLED DENTINE.

BESIDES DENTINE, THE CROWN IS COVERED BY ENAMEL. ENAMEL IS THE HARDEST SUBSTANCE YOU CAN FIND IN YOUR BODY.

PSSST...READERS, HERE'S HOW YOU CAN GET HOLES IN YOUR TEETH... AND ALSO TOOTHACHE.

IF YOU WANT HOLES IN YOUR TEETH, THE FIRST THING YOU HAVE TO DO IS GET RID OF THE ENAMEL ON THE CROWNS OF YOUR TEETH.

HOW DO YOU GET RID OF THE ENAMEL?

EASY.

ALL YOU DO IS LET PIECES OF FOOD, ESPECIALLY SWEETS, STAY BETWEEN YOUR TEETH AFTER YOU'VE EATEN.

YOU MAY THINK YOUR MOUTH IS CLEAN. BUT IT IS ALWAYS FULL OF BACTERIA. BACTERIA PRODUCE ACIDS OUT OF THE FOOD STUCK BETWEEN YOUR TEETH.

WHAT DO THE ACIDS DO?

THEY DISSOLVE A LITTLE OF THE ENAMEL.

IF YOU DO NOT CLEAN YOUR TEETH THE ENAMEL WILL BE GRADUALLY EATEN AWAY BY THE ACIDS FORMED IN THE MOUTH.

ONCE THE ENAMEL IS GONE, THE BACTERIA CAN GET AT THE LAYER UNDERNEATH IT, THE DENTINE.

IF NOT STOPPED THEY'LL EAT THEIR WAY THROUGH THE DENTINE RIGHT UP TO THE PULP.

NOW YOU HAVE A NICE HOLE IN YOUR TOOTH.

EVERY TIME YOU DRINK SOMETHING TOO COLD OR EAT SOMETHING TOO HOT, THE NERVES IN THE PULP WILL GET IRRITATED AND CAUSE A TOOTHACHE.

HOLE FORMED IN TOOTH

GIGANTIC BUBBLES

Things required:

Glycerine – 12 drops

Water

Any detergent powder (heaped teaspoons)

A large dish

Aluminium hanger – 1

To get your bubbles:

Pour the water, soap and glycerine into the dish. Stir well.

Twist the hanger into a round shape!

Dip the circular part of the hanger into the dish to get a soapy film.

Blow gently to get king sized bubbles.

CHAMATAKA GETS A HAT!

THIS GRASS IS SO JUICY AND SWEET.

WHAT'S THAT? I THOUGHT I HEARD A SOUND.

BANG

HUNTERS!

OOOPS!

I THINK I GOT HIM.

YES, HE'S LIMPING.

DON'T SHOOT! A LIVE DEER SHOULD FETCH US A BETTER PRICE THAN A DEAD ONE. I'LL RUN AFTER HIM AND CATCH HIM.

OOOPS !

HEY !

!!!!

I...I'M SORRY ! I...

WOULD YOU PLEASE GET OFF ME ?!

Y...YES !

YOU OKAY, BUTTER ? YOU LOOK WEIRD !

DO YOU KNOW WHO THE GUY I FELL ON WAS ?!

WHO ?!

IT WAS RUSSEL ! THE LEAD SINGER OF THE ROCK BAND, THE HEEBEE JEEBEES !

THEY PLAYED AT OUR SCHOOL ASSEMBLY, REMEMBER?

OH YEAH!

BUT WHAT'S A ROCK STAR LIKE HIM DOING IN A SMALL VILLAGE LIKE HARIYALI?

I DON'T KNOW BUT I'M NOT BRAVE ENOUGH TO ASK HIM RIGHT NOW!

YEAH...HE DIDN'T LOOK VERY HAPPY WHEN YOU SAT ON HIM!

I HOPE HE CALMS DOWN LATER...THEN WE CAN TRY TALKING TO HIM!

AFTER A LONG AND BUMPY RIDE, THE BUS REACHED HARIYALI –

DADA!

KIRAN! HOW I'VE MISSED YOU!

AMAR, GOOD TO SEE YOU TOO!

LIKEWISE, SIR!

66

DADA, YOU WON'T BELIEVE WHO WAS IN THE BUS WITH US!

BALU WITH HIS PET GOAT?

NOPE! A REAL LIVE ROCK STAR, THAT'S WHO!

LOOK, THERE HE IS! GETTING INTO THAT COOL JEEP!

DO YOU THINK ANYONE ELSE WILL RECOGNISE RUSSEL BESIDES US?

IN THIS VILLAGE? NOT A CHANCE! ONLY YOU KIDS ARE EXCITED ABOUT THESE LONG-HAIRED NOISEMAKERS!

BUT DADA WAS WRONG —

LALU! THAT'S HIM!

YES, BOSS!

WE'RE GOING TO GET RUSSEL IF THAT'S THE LAST THING WE DO!

(GASP!)

KIRAN! DID YOU HEAR?! THOSE TWO MEN KNOW RUSSEL...AND THEY'RE OUT TO GET HIM!

DO YOU THINK HE'S IN DANGER?!

THE NEXT DAY, THEY SET OFF FOR THE TRIPLE STAR FARMHOUSE –

WATCH YOUR STEP, BUTTER! WE CAN'T AFFORD TO GET INTO ANY MORE TROUBLE!

I KNOW! WE'LL JUST WARN RUSSEL AND GO!

HEY, KIDS! HAVE YOU SEEN A LONG-HAIRED FELLOW WITH A BASEBALL CAP AROUND HERE?

(GASP!)

YEAH...HE'S ON THE OTHER SIDE OF THE FARM! PAST THE FLOCK OF GOATS!

THANKS!

MOVE, YOU BLEATING BEASTS!

BAAA! BAAA!

HONK! HONK!

HAH! THAT OUGHT TO DELAY THEM FOR A WHILE!

AT LEAST UNTIL WE FIND RUSSEL OURSELVES!

BUT THAT WAS EASIER SAID THAN DONE –

DRAT! RUSSEL ISN'T IN THE FARMHOUSE!

HE ISN'T EVEN ON THE FARM!

HELP SOON CAME –

YOU BOYS HAD BETTER EXPLAIN EVERYTHING !

HIS CAP... (SOB !) POOR RUSSEL, POOR HEEBEE JEEBEES !

(SNIFF !)

IT'S TOO TRAGIC ! SO YOUNG...AND GONE SO SOON !

HEY ! THAT'S MY CAP ! THANK GOD YOU FOUND IT !

RUSSEL !

YOU'RE ALIVE !

OF COURSE I AM ! WHY SHOULDN'T I BE ?!

NO...WE THOUGHT THAT YOU...YOU HAD BEEN DROWNED IN THE WELL !

SAY, AREN'T YOU THE SAME KID WHO FELL ON ME...

ER...NEVER MIND THAT ! HOW DID YOUR CAP GET IN THERE ?

A STRONG WIND BLEW IT OFF MY HEAD YESTERDAY AND I THOUGHT I'D LOST IT FOREVER!

I'M THRILLED YOU FOUND THE CAP! I KEEP ALL MY NEWEST SONG LYRICS IN A SECRET COMPARTMENT INSIDE IT!

IT'S A GOOD THING YOUR CAP'S WATER-PROOF!

AND IT'S AN EVEN BETTER THING THAT YOU TWO FOUND IT!

RUSSEL! THERE YOU ARE! WE'VE BEEN LOOKING FOR YOU EVERYWHERE!

WE WOULD HAVE FOUND YOU SOONER IF THESE BOYS HADN'T SENT US ON A WILD GOOSE CHASE!

(ULP!)

WILL YOU CONSIDER SIGNING A CONTRACT WITH US TO PERFORM A SERIES OF CONCERTS? WE'LL MAKE IT WORTH YOUR WHILE!

LET'S DISCUSS IT! NOW THAT I'VE FOUND MY NEW SONGS, THE HEEBEE JEEBEES CAN PUT ON A GREAT SHOW!

AND YOU TWO WILL GET FRONT ROW SEATS TO ALL OF THEM!

WOO HOO!

ROCK ON!